Universal Edition

easy BLUE piano

Mike Cornick

www.universaledition.com
vienna · london · new york

UE 21 260
ISMN M-008-07544-5
UPC 8-03452-02276-3
ISBN 978-3-7024-2735-1

Vorwort

Nach dem Erfolg von *Blue Piano* (UE 19762 – veröffentlicht 1993) wurde diese neue Sammlung in der Hoffnung zusammengestellt, mit leichteren Stücken die Aufmerksamkeit jener Pianisten auf sich zu ziehen, die erst vor kurzem mit dem Klavierspiel begonnen haben. Die stilistische Breite in dem hier vorliegenden Band ist auch etwas umfangreicher als in der Sammlung *Blue Piano*, die sich auf die Swingballade beschränkte. *Easy Blue Piano* enthält auch Stücke mit Achtelnoten, die gleichmäßig (oder „on-beat") gespielt werden, sowie diverse Jazz-Walzer, einen Country-Blues, einen kurzen Ausflug zum 5/4-Takt und Titel in mittlerem bis mäßig schnellem Tempo. *Cool Blues*, das letzte Stück dieser Sammlung, hält sich viel stärker an den Stil des ursprünglichen Heftes *Blue Piano* und kann als Brücke zwischen den beiden Ausgaben verstanden werden.

Die Auswahl der Tonarten wurde absichtlich leicht gehalten, selten steht ein Stück in einer Tonart mit mehr als einem Be- oder zwei Kreuz-Vorzeichen.

Mein Dank richtet sich an einige junge PianistInnen, die frühe Fassungen von einigen dieser Stücke ausprobiert haben: Cleo und Cory Jones waren die Ersten, die *Things Past*, *Autumn Colours*, *Wood-Sheddin'* und *A Quiet Corner* gespielt haben. Suzy Brown und Ella Price interpretierten als Erste *Love Those Blues*. Ihre Bemerkungen über diese Stücke erwiesen sich als hilfreich und bestätigend.

April 2004   Mike Cornick

Préface

Après le succès de *Blue Piano* (UE 19762, publication en 1993), ce nouveau recueil a été composé avec l'espoir d'attirer l'attention des pianistes qui n'ont commencé le piano que récemment et ce, par l'intermédiaire de pièces plus faciles. La variété stylistique dont fait montre le présent volume est également un peu plus étendue que dans le volume *Blue Piano* qui se limitait à la ballade swing. *Easy Blue Piano* contient également des pièces en croches qui sont jouées de manière homogène (ou « on-beat »), ainsi que diverses valses jazz, un Country-Blues, une courte excursion en mesure à 5/4 et un titre composé dans un tempo moyen à modérément rapide. *Cool Blues*, la dernière pièce de ce recueil, s'en tient plus fortement au style du cahier originel *Blue Piano* et peut être envisagé comme un pont entre les deux éditions.

Le choix des tonalités s'est volontairement limité à un niveau facile, il est rare qu'un morceau soit écrit dans une tonalité comportant plus d'un bémol ou de deux dièses.

Mes remerciements vont aux pianistes qui ont essayé des versions précoces de quelques-unes de ces pièces : Cleo et Cory Jones ont été les premiers à jouer *Things Past, Autumn Colors, Wood-Sheddin'* et *A Quiet Corner*. Suzy Brown et Ella Price ont interprété les premières *Love Those Blues*. Leurs remarques sur ces pièces se sont avérées riches et judicieuses.

Avril 2004   Mike Cornick

Preface

Following the success of *Blue Piano* (UE 19762 – published in 1993), this new collection of pieces has been compiled in the hope of engaging the attention of pianists who are at an earlier stage of learning. The stylistic scope of this collection is also somewhat broader than that of *Blue Piano* which confined itself to swing ballads; *Easy Blue Piano* also includes even-quaver (or "on-beat") pieces as well as jazz waltzes, a country blues, a brief excursion into 5/4, and some medium or medium-to-up-tempo numbers. *Cool Blues*, the final piece in the collection, is much more in the style of the original *Blue Piano* volume and might be seen as a bridge between the two publications.

The choice of key signatures has been deliberately restricted and does not exceed one flat or two sharps.

My thanks are due to some young pianists who tried out the first drafts of some of these pieces: Cleo and Cory Jones were the first to play *Things Past*, *Autumn Colours*, *Wood-Sheddin'* and *A Quiet Corner*, and Suzy Brown and Ella Price were the first to play *Love Those Blues*. Their comments on these pieces have proved to be both helpful and encouraging.

April 2004   Mike Cornick

Contents · Inhalt · Table des Matières

Things Past

Mike Cornick

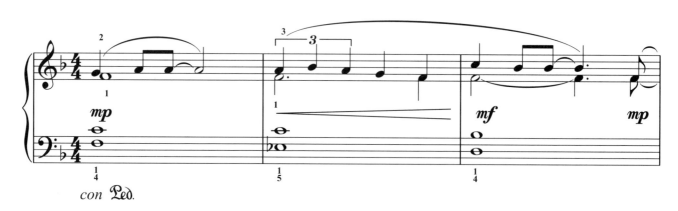

con Ped.

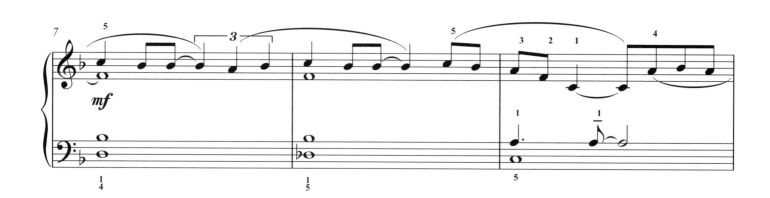

Universal Edition UE 21 260

Love Those Blues

Mike Cornick

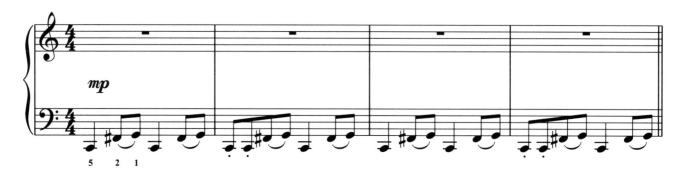

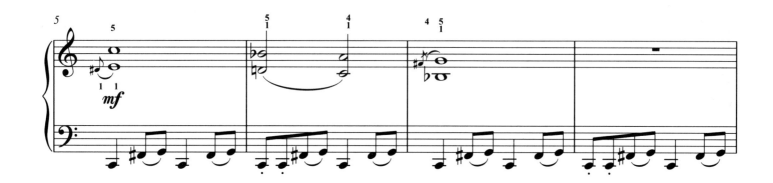

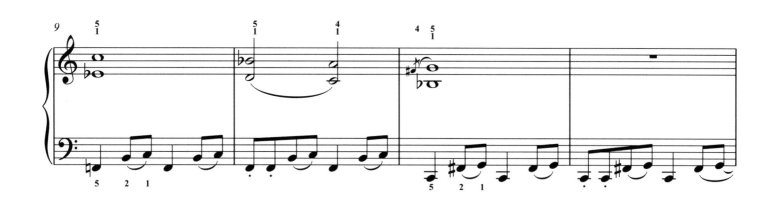

Autumn Colours

Mike Cornick

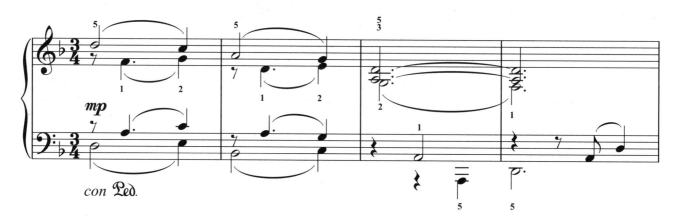

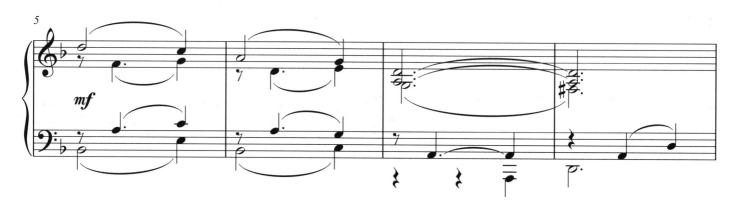

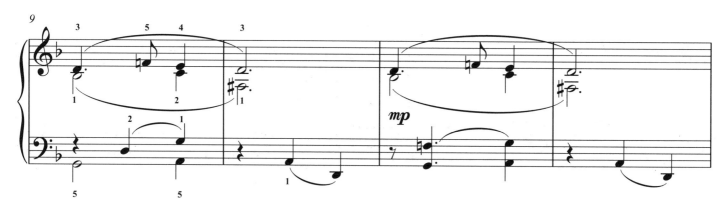

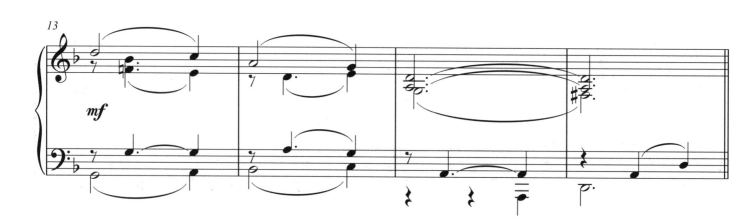

Wood-Sheddin'

Mike Cornick

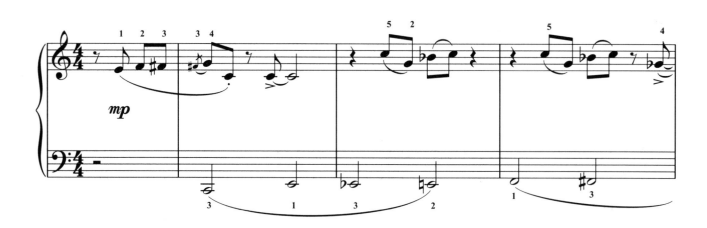

A Quiet Corner

Mike Cornick

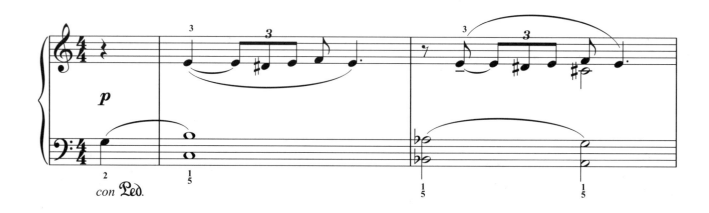

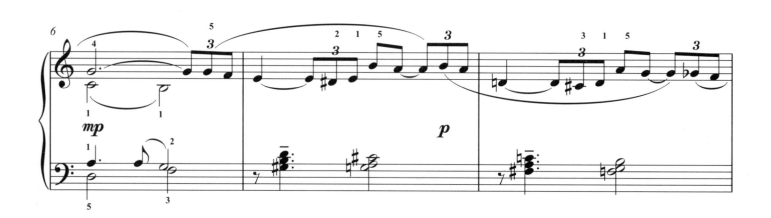

Just Cruisin'

Mike Cornick

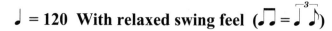

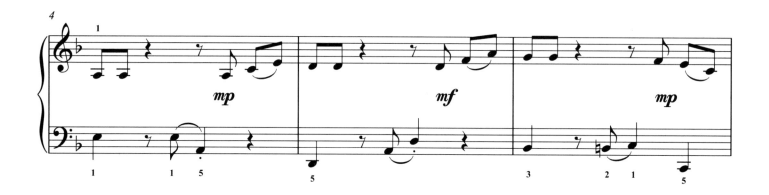

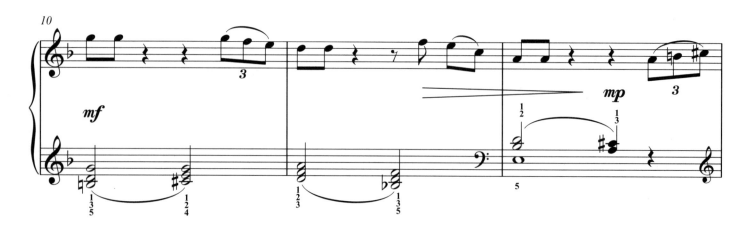

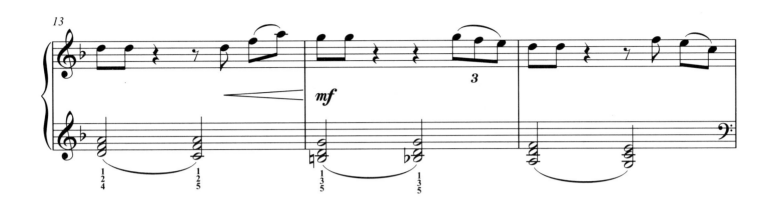

Three Into Five

[A variant of *Quintessence* from *Pianojazz Skillbuilder 3* – UE 21 079]

Mike Cornick

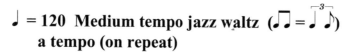

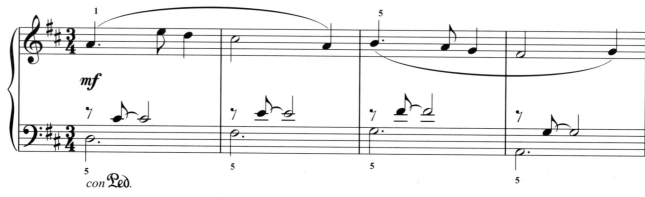

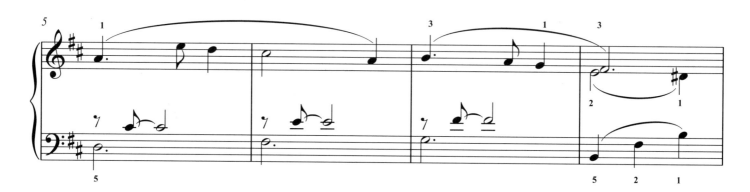

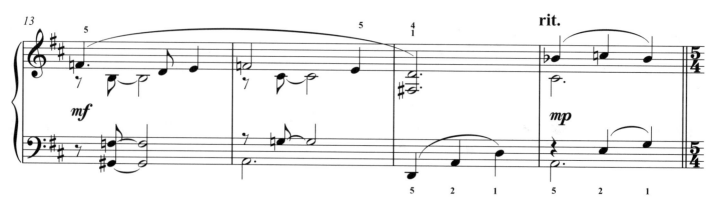

Country and Western Blues

Mike Cornick

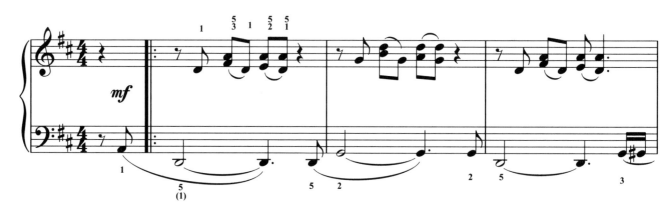

A Solent Breeze

Mike Cornick

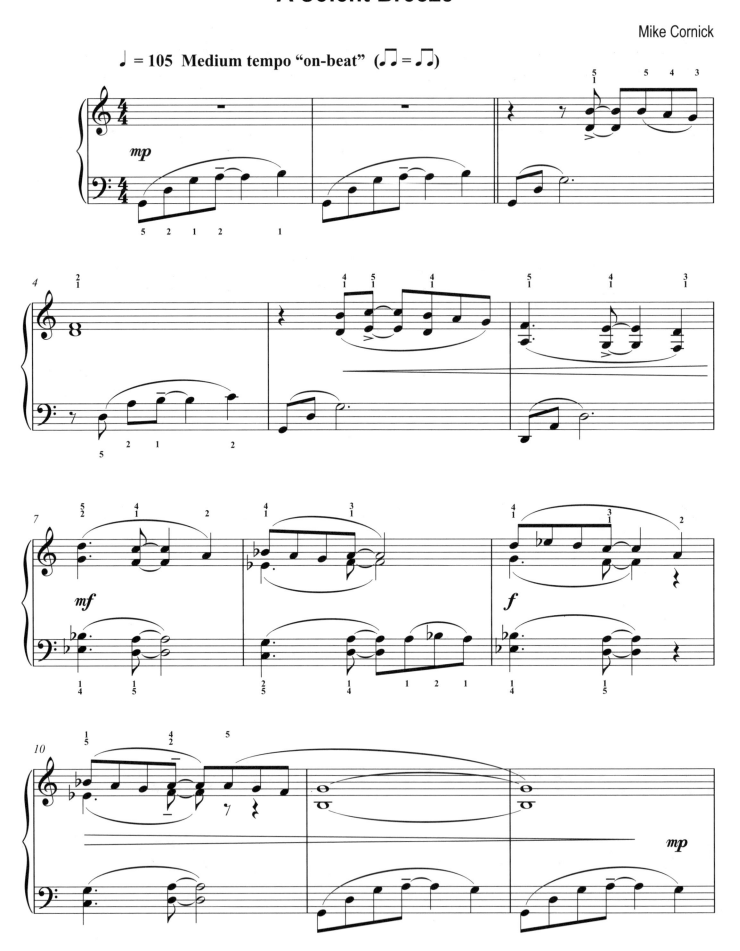

Cool Blues

Mike Cornick

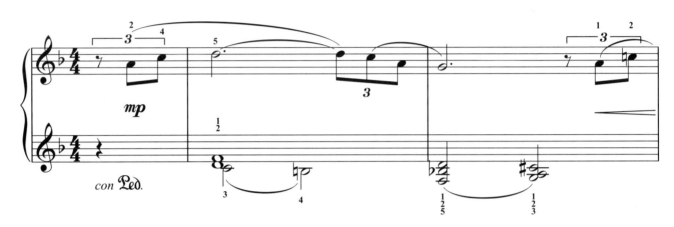

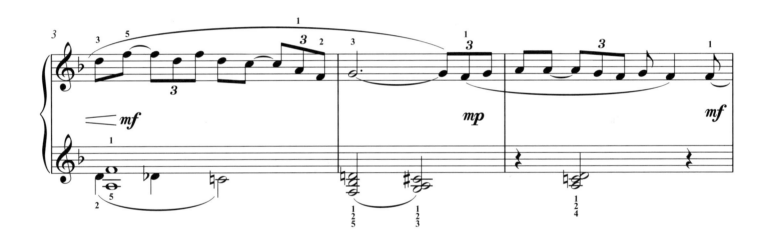

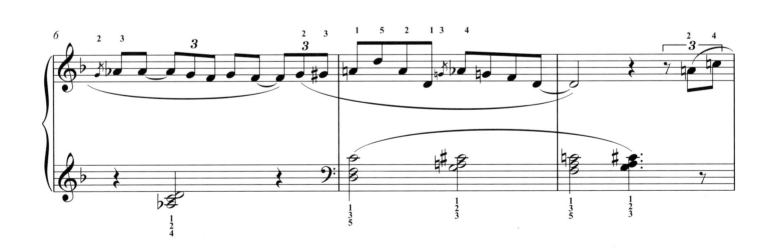

Performance Directions

The direction (♫ = ♫) means that quavers (eighth notes) are to be played evenly, as written.

The direction (♫ = ♩♪) means that quavers (eighth notes) are to be played with a swing feel.

E.g. ♫♫ should be played ♩♪♩♪

and ♪ ♫ should be played ₹ ♪♩♪

The degree of swing which the player applies to quaver (eighth note) movement, however, is a matter of interpretation and need not be treated with absolute mathematical precision.

Aufführungshinweise

Das Zeichen (♫ = ♫) bedeutet, dass die Achtelnoten genau so gespielt werden, wie sie notiert sind.

Das Zeichen (♫ = ♩♪) bedeutet, dass die Achtelnoten mit „Swing Feeling" gespielt werden.

D. h. ♫♫ sollte so gespielt werden ♩♪♩♪

und ♪ ♫ sollte so gespielt werden ₹ ♪♩♪

Das Maß an triolischer Rhythmisierung, das der Spieler der Achtelbewegung gibt, ist eine Frage der Interpretation und braucht nicht mit absoluter mathematischer Präzision behandelt zu werden.

Indications pour l'exécution

Le signe (♫ = ♫) signifie que les croches doivent être jouées exactement comme elles sont notées.

Le signe (♫ = ♩♪) signifie que le croches sont jouées avec une « sensibilité swing ».

C'est-à-dire que ♫♫ devrait être joué ainsi ♩♪♩♪

et que ♪ ♫ devrait être joué ainsi ₹ ♪♩♪

Le degré de balancement que l'exécutant applique au mouvement de croche est, quoi qu'il en soit, une question d'interprétation et ne doit pas être traité avec une absolue précision mathématique.